Poems 2

edited by
Michael Harrison and
Christopher Stuart-Clark

Oxford University Press

Oxford University Press, Walton Street, Oxford OX2 6DP
Oxford New York Toronto
Delhi Bombay Calcutta Madras Karachi
Petaling Jaya Singapore Hong Kong Tokyo
Nairobi Dar es Salaam Cape Town
Melbourne Auckland

and associated companies in
Berlin Ibadan

Oxford is a trade mark of Oxford University Press

First published 1980
Reprinted 1982, 1983, 1985, 1987, 1989, 1991

ISBN 0 19 834268 3

Printed in Hong Kong

Contents

The publishers would like to thank the following people for permission to reproduce copyright material:

Animal Graphics for 26; Ardea for 31; Arctic Camera for 100–101; Janet and Colin Bord for 18–21, 28; British Rail (Western Region) for 48–49; British Tourist Authority for 32, 80; Maurice Carroll for 108; CEGB for 67; COI for 86–87 (Crown Copyright); Commonwealth War Graves Commission for 82–83; Hunter Cordaiy for 14–15, 42–43, 120; the Dean and Chapter of Ely Cathedral for 44; Nick Fogden for 10–11, 16–17, 36, 58, 61, 78, 90–91, 114; Fay Godwin for 107, 112, 115; Greater London Council for 104; Sue Heap for 29, 56; ITN for 12–13; Lawrence Lawry for 88, 92–93; Barry Lewis for 33, 62, 64, 68–69, 71, 96–97; Nick Lyons for 44; Maurice Nimmo for 52–53, 55; Oxford Mail for 75; Press Association for 103; Mrs Amoret Scott for 8–9; John Topham Picture Library for 34–35; Simon Warner for 46–47, 76, 94–95; Rita Winstanley for 37, 66.

The publishers would also like to thank Mrs L. Holmes and Relko for their kind assistance with some photographs.

There was a young man from Bengal
Who went to a fancy dress ball;
He thought he would risk it
And go as a biscuit,
But a dog ate him up in the hall.

A man on the flying trapeze
Emitted a terrible sneeze.
The consequent force
Shot him right off his course,
And they found him next day in some trees.

'Open wide,' said a dentist called Bert
To a man-eating shark whose teeth hurt.
'When I've finished the drilling
I'll give you a filling.'
He did – and the filling was Bert.

Said a buffalo hunter in Streatham,
'There are buffaloes here and I'll get 'em,
There's no need to fret
If you've not seen 'em yet –
They're around, but you've simply not met 'em.'

6

There was a young lady from Ryde
Who ate a green apple and died;
The apple fermented
Inside the lamented,
And made cider inside her inside.

There was an old man from Nantucket
Who kept all his cash in a bucket.
His daughter, named Nan,
Ran away with a man,
And as for the bucket, Nan tucket.

There once was a girl, Laura Norder,
Went out with Bill Posters, who bored 'er,
They met Eva Brick
She'd been in the nick,
But her boyfriend, Van Dal, still adored 'er.

There was a young man of Japan
Who wrote verse that never would scan.
When they said 'But the thing
Doesn't go with a swing,
He said, 'Yes, but I always like to get as many words into the last line as I possibly can.

On Leslie Moore

Here lies what's left
Of Leslie Moore.
No Les
No more.

On Sir John Guise

Here lies the body of Sir John Guise,
Nobody laughs and nobody cries;
Where his soul is, and how it fares,
Nobody knows and nobody cares.

On Dr. Chard

Here lies the corpse of Doctor Chard,
Who'd fill'd half of this churchyard.

On a Dentist

Stranger, approach this spot with gravity;
John Brown is filling his last cavity.

On a Man Named Merideth

Here lies one blown out of breath,
Who lived a merry life, and died a Merideth.

On a Liar

Even my tombstone gives the truth away,
It says to all who face this little hill
'Hic iacet': 'Here I lie'. Or should it say
Here I lie – still?

On John Ford's Wife

Here lies Mary – the wife of John Ford.
We hope her soul is gone to the Lord.
But if for Hell she has changed this life,
She had better be there than John Ford's wife.

On a 'Shrew'

Here lies my poor wife, much lamented,
She is happy and I am contented.

Midland Epitaph

'Er as was 'as gone from me.
Us as is 'll go ter she.

Here lies I, no wonder I'm dead,
For a broad-wheel'd waggon went over my head.

On Sir John Vanbrugh (The Architect)

Under this stone, Reader, survey
Dead Sir John Vanbrugh's house of clay.
Lie heavy on him, Earth! For he
Laid many heavy loads on thee!

I went to the doctor, yes,
I went to him
and I said – 'Doctor, Doctor,
it's Roads,' I said. 'Roads?' he says.
'Roads,' I said.
'No such thing,' he says.
'I've got Roads, Doctor,
very bad Roads.
I've got long distance lorryworry
one way only lorryworry.
They say:
No U-turns Ahead.
I know I turned my head,
but I saw a zebra crossing
and a bus eating a traffic jam.
I can hear
unhappy new gears.
When traffic's light
at traffic lights
I see red
amber
red and amber
red already.

I wish I was a
windscreen wiper.
Once I washed windscreens
now I watch wipers.
What shall I do?
I've got Roads,
very bad Roads, Doctor.
What shall I do?'

So he looked at me and said:
'I don't know what I know
but I've got just the stink for you.'
and he squeezed me on the Underground
And handed me the tube.

Michael Rosen

Here is the News:

In Manchester today a man was seen
with hair on top of his head.
Over now straightway to our Northern correspondent:
Hugh Snews.

'It's been a really incredible day
here in Manchester. Scenes like this
have been seen here everyday
for years and years. It's now quite certain
no one will be saying anything about this
for months to come. One eyewitness said so.
"Are you sure?" I said.
She said: "No."
Back to you in London.'

All round the world,
newspapers, radio and television
have taken no notice of this story
and already a Prime Minister
has said nothing about it at all.
What next?
Rumour McRumourbungle,
Expert expert in expert experts?

'I doubt it. I doubt whether
anyone *will* doubt it – but I do.'

'What?'

'Doubt it.'

Thank you, Rumour McRumourbungle.
But how did it all begin?
As dawn broke in Manchester it soon became clear.
It's quite likely there was a lot of air in the air.
An hour after a few minutes had gone,
a couple of seconds passed
and a minute later at 12.15
it was a quarter past twelve.
Suddenly from across the other side of the road,
on the side facing this side,
there was the same road from the other side.
This side was now facing that side
and the road on that other side
was still opposite this.
Then – it happened
There is no question of this.
In fact – no one has questioned it at all.
Further proof of this comes from the police
who say that a woman held for questioning
was released immediately
because she didn't know any of the answers
to the questions that no one asked her . . .

So –
it's something of a mystery.
Yes –
it's a mysterious thing to some
and there are some who think
it could
in a mysterious way
be nothing at all.

Michael Rosen

The Forlorn Sea

Our Princess married
A fairy King,
It was a sensational
Wedding.

Now they live in a palace
Of porphyry,
Far, far away,
By the fòrlorn sea.

Sometimes people visit them,
Last week they invited me;
That is how I can tell you
They live by a fòrlorn sea.

(They said: Here's a magic carpet,
Come on this,
And when you arrive
We will give you a big kiss.)

I play in the palace garden,
I climb the sycamore tree,
Sometimes I swim
In the fòrlorn sea.

The King and the Princess are shadowy,
Yet beautiful,
They are waited on by white cats,
Who are dutiful.

It is like a dream
When they kiss and cuddle me,
But I like it, I like it,
I do not wish to break free.

So I eat all they give me
Because I have read
If you eat fairy food
You will never wake up in your own bed,

But will go on living,
As has happened to me,
Far, far away
By a forlorn sea.

Stevie Smith

Advice to a Knight

Wear modest armour; and walk quietly
In woods, where any noise is treacherous.
Avoid dragons and deceptive maidens.

Be polite to other men in armour,
Especially the fierce ones, who are often strong.
Treat all old men as they might be magicians.

So you may come back from you wanderings,
Clink proud and stiff into the queen's court
To doff your helmet and expect her thanks.

The young queen is amused at your white hair,
Asks you to show your notched and rusty sword,
And orders extra straw for your bedding.

Tomorrow put on your oldest clothes,
Take a stout stick and set off again,
It's safer that way if no more rewarding.

T. H. Jones

Old English Riddle

I'm by nature solitary, scarred by spear
and wounded by sword, weary of battle.
I frequently see the face of war, and fight
hateful enemies; yet I hold no hope
of help being brought to me in the battle,
before I'm eventually done to death.
In the stronghold of the city sharp-edged swords,
skilfully forged in the flame by smiths,
bite deeply into me. I can but await
a more fearsome encounter; it is not for me
to discover in the city any of those doctors
who heal grievous wounds with roots and herbs.
The scars from sword wounds gape wider and wider;
death blows are dealt me by day and by night.

Translated by Kevin Crossley-Holland

Goody Blake and Harry Gill
A True Story

Oh! what's the matter? what's the matter?
What is't that ails young Harry Gill?
That evermore his teeth they chatter,
Chatter, chatter, chatter still!
At night, at morning, and at noon,
'Tis all the same with Harry Gill;
Beneath the sun, beneath the moon,
His teeth they chatter, chatter still!

Young Harry was a lusty drover,
And who so stout of limb as he?
His cheeks were red as ruddy clover;
His voice was like the voice of three.
Old Goody Blake was old and poor;
Ill fed she was, and thinly clad;
And any man who passed her door
Might see how poor a hut she had.

Remote from sheltered village-green,
On a hill's northern side she dwelt,
Where from sea-blasts the hawthorns lean,
And hoary dews are slow to melt.
'Twas well enough, when summer came,
The long, warm, lightsome summer-day,
Then at her door the canty Dame
Would sit, as any linnet, gay.

But when the ice our streams did fetter,
Oh then how her old bones would shake!
You would have said, if you had met her,
'Twas a hard time for Goody Blake.
Her evenings then were dull and dead:
Sad case it was, as you may think,
For very cold to go to bed;
And then for cold not sleep a wink.

Now, when the frost was past enduring,
And made her poor old bones to ache,
Could anything be more alluring
Than the old hedge to Goody Blake?
And now and then, it must be said,
When her old bones were cold and chill,
She left her fire or left her bed,
To seek the hedge of Harry Gill.

Now Harry he had long suspected
This trespass of old Goody Blake;
And vowed that she should be detected –
That he on her would vengeance take.
And oft from his warm fire he'd go,
And to the fields his road would take,
And there, at night, in frost and snow,
He watch'd to seize old Goody Blake.

And once, behind a rick of barley,
Thus looking out did Harry stand:
The moon was full and shining clearly,
And crisp with frost the stubble land.
– He hears a noise – he's all awake –
Again? – on tip-toe down the hill
He softly creeps – 'tis Goody Blake;
She's at the hedge of Harry Gill!

Right glad was he when he beheld her:
Stick after stick did Goody pull,
He stood behind a bush of elder,
Till she had filled her apron full.
When with her load she turned about,
The by-way back again to take;
He started forward, with a shout,
And sprang upon poor Goody Blake.

And fiercely by the arm he took her,
And by the arm he held her fast,
And fiercely by the arm he shook her,
And cried, 'I've caught you then at last!'
Then Goody, who had nothing said,
Her bundle from her lap let fall;
And kneeling on the sticks, she prayed
To God that is the judge of all.

She prayed, her withered hand uprearing,
While Harry held her by the arm –
'God! who are never out of hearing,
O may he never more be warm!'
The cold, cold moon above her head,
Thus on her knees did Goody pray;
Young Harry heard what she had said:
And icy cold he turned away.

He went complaining all the morrow
That he was cold and very chill:
His face was gloom, his heart was sorrow,
Alas! that day for Harry Gill!
And Harry's flesh it fell away;
And all who see him say, 'tis plain,
That, live as long as live he may,
He never will be warm again.

No word to any man he utters,
A-bed or up, to young or old;
But ever to himself he mutters,
'Poor Harry Gill is very cold.'
A-bed or up, by night or day;
His teeth they chatter, chatter still.
Now think, ye farmers all, I pray,
Of Goody Blake and Harry Gill!

William Wordsworth

Saturdays I put on my boots and go wading
    down the River Pinn
singing songs like: Olly Jonathan Curly and Carrot
past garden trees, the back of shops, building sites
scaffolds and timber, park-keepers' huts
the disused railway line and the new estate
the garage junk heap, twenty foot high in greasy
    springs
unstuffed car-seats, boxes in thousands
light bulbs, rubber stamps and an old typewriter,
through the woods where the woodpeckers used to be
and there are rapids and bogs and sand-flats,
you have to watch for hidden jaws in the mud
or beaver dams and Amazon settlements;
you can see into the back of the telephone exchange
to a million wires on the walls
and an all-red telephone
and there's Grolly's Grotto:
the tunnel under the library under the cleaners
under the bicycle sheds and the newspaper stand.
In the middle it smells black,
you can't see either end
the walls are wet and the water's deeper
where Thatcher fell in and under
and screamed for hours so it echoed and echoed
but we couldn't see him –

all we could hear was him splashing and thrashing
hitting the walls with his boots
us holding on to the mucky bricks
bumping into each other's arms
or shouting and shushing until it went quiet
and still in the dark. And then we ran.
Or swam. And fought. It was miles.
Rushed into the light covered in slime
looking at each other with eyes big and silly:
Where's Thatcher?
No one said we'd left him. Just us goggling –
waiting for a splosh or scud.
It was raining where we stood
goggling in the light under the library where it was
    warm
not knowing that Thatcher was crawling out the other
    end

Michael Rosen

The Galloping Cat

Oh I am a cat that likes to
Gallop about doing good
So
One day when I was
Galloping about doing good, I saw
A Figure in the path; I said:
Get off! (Be-
   cause
I am a cat that likes to
Gallop about doing good)
But he did not move, instead
He raised his hand as if
To land me a cuff
So I made to dodge so as to
Prevent him bringing it orf,
Un-for-tune-ately I slid
On a banana skin
Some Ass had left instead
Of putting in the bin. So
His hand caught me on the cheek
I tried
To lay his arm open from wrist to elbow
With my sharp teeth
Because I am
A cat that likes to gallop about doing good.
Would you believe it?
He wasn't there
My teeth met nothing but air,
But a Voice said: Poor cat,
(Meaning me) and a soft stroke
Came on me head
Since when I have been bald.
I regard myself as
A martyr to doing good.

Also I heard a swoosh
As of wings, and saw
A halo shining at the height of
Mrs Gubbin's backyard fence,
So I thought: What's the good
Of galloping about doing good
When angels stand in the path
And do not do as they should
Such as having an arm to be bitten off.
All the same I
Intend to go on being
A cat that likes to
Gallop about doing good
So
With my bald head I go,
Chopping the untidy flowers down, to and fro,
An' scooping up the grass to show
Underneath
The cinderpath of wrath
Ha ha ha ha, ho,
Angels aren't the only who do not know
What's what and that
Galloping about doing good
Is a full-time job
That needs
An experienced eye of earthly
Sharpness, worth I dare say
(If you'll forgive a personal note)
A good deal more
Than all that skyey stuff
Of angels that make so bold as
To pity a cat like me that
Gallops about doing good.

Stevie Smith

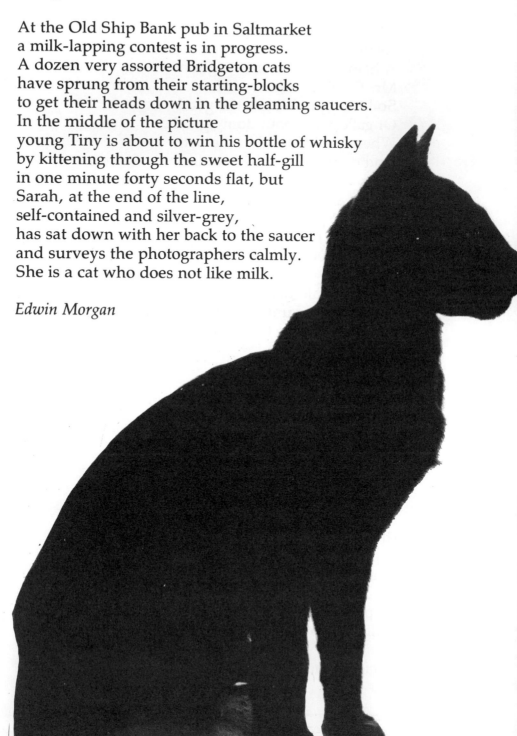

Glasgow October 1972

At the Old Ship Bank pub in Saltmarket
a milk-lapping contest is in progress.
A dozen very assorted Bridgeton cats
have sprung from their starting-blocks
to get their heads down in the gleaming saucers.
In the middle of the picture
young Tiny is about to win his bottle of whisky
by kittening through the sweet half-gill
in one minute forty seconds flat, but
Sarah, at the end of the line,
self-contained and silver-grey,
has sat down with her back to the saucer
and surveys the photographers calmly.
She is a cat who does not like milk.

Edwin Morgan

Milk for the Cat

When the tea is brought at five o'clock,
And all the neat curtains are drawn with care,
The little black cat with bright green eyes
Is suddenly purring there.

At first she pretends, having nothing to do,
She has come in merely to blink by the grate,
But, though tea may be late or the milk may be sour
She is never late.

And presently her agate eyes
Take a soft, large, milky haze
And her independent casual glance
Becomes a stiff, hard gaze.

Then she stamps her claws or lifts her ears,
Or twists her tail and begins to stir,
Till suddenly all her lithe body becomes
One breathing, trembling purr.

The children eat and wriggle and laugh,
The two old ladies stroke their silk:
But the cat is grown small and thin with desire,
Transformed to a creeping lust for milk.

The white saucer like some full moon descends
At last from the clouds of the table above;
She sighs and dreams and thrills and glows,
Transfigured with love.

She nestles over the shining rim,
Buries her chin in the creamy sea;
Her tail hangs loose; each drowsy paw
Is doubled under each bending knee.

[cont

A long, dim ecstasy holds her life;
Her world is an infinite shapeless white,
Till her tongue has curled the last holy drop,
Then she sinks back into the night,

Draws and dips her body to heap
Her sleepy nerves in the great arm-chair,
Lies defeated and buried deep
Three or four hours unconscious there.

Harold Monro

A Widow Bird

A widow bird sate mourning for her love
   Upon a wintry bough;
The frozen wind crept on above,
   The freezing stream below.

There was no leaf upon the forest bare,
   No flower upon the ground,
And little motion in the air
   Except the mill-wheel's sound.

Percy Bysshe Shelley

Fetching Cows

The black one, last as usual, swings her head
And coils a black tongue round a grass-tuft. I
Watch her soft weight come down, her split feet
        spread.

In front, the others swing and slouch; they roll
Their great Greek eyes and breathe out milky gusts
From muzzles black and shiny as wet coal.

The collie trots, bored, at my heels, then plops
Into the ditch. The sea makes a tired sound
That's always stopping though it never stops.

A haycart squats prickeared against the sky.
Hay breath and milk breath. Far out in the West
The wrecked sun founders though its colours fly.

The collie's bored. There's nothing to control . . .
And the black cow is two native carriers
Bringing its belly home, slung from a pole.

Norman MacCaig

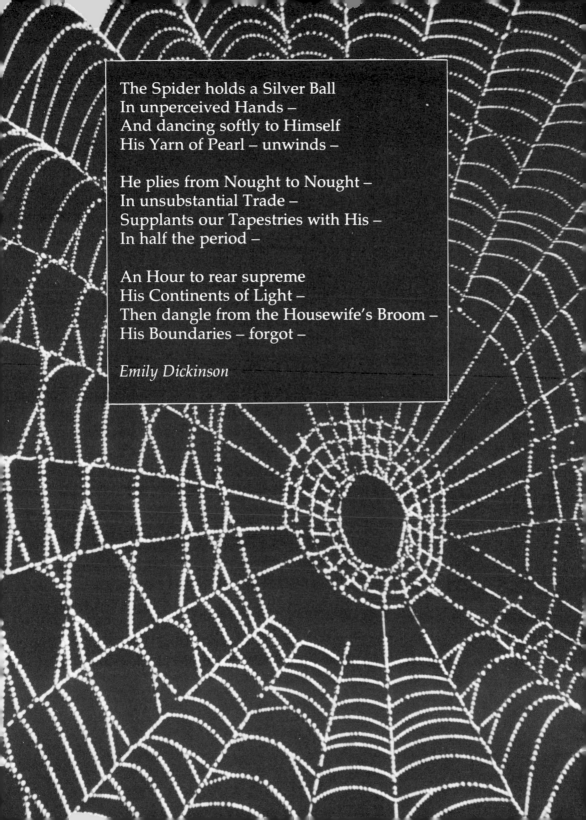

The Spider holds a Silver Ball
In unperceived Hands –
And dancing softly to Himself
His Yarn of Pearl – unwinds –

He plies from Nought to Nought –
In unsubstantial Trade –
Supplants our Tapestries with His –
In half the period –

An Hour to rear supreme
His Continents of Light –
Then dangle from the Housewife's Broom –
His Boundaries – forgot –

Emily Dickinson

The Wind begun to rock the Grass
With threatening Tunes and low –
He threw a Menace at the Earth –
A Menace at the Sky.

The Leaves unhooked themselves from Trees –
And started all abroad
The Dust did scoop itself like Hands
And threw away the Road.

The Wagons quickened on the Streets
The Thunder hurried slow –
The Lightning showed a Yellow Beak
And then a livid Claw.

The Birds put up the Bars to Nests –
The Cattle fled to Barns –
There came one drop of Giant Rain
And then as if the Hands

That held the Dams had parted hold
The Waters Wrecked the Sky,
But overlooked my Father's House –
Just quartering a Tree –

Emily Dickinson

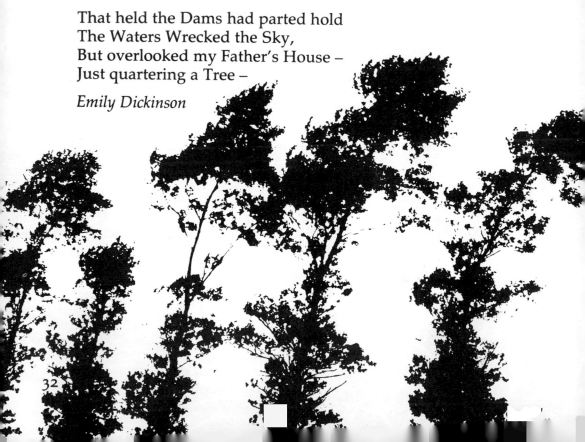

Child on Top of a Greenhouse

The wind billowing out the seat of my britches,
My feet crackling splinters of glass and dried putty,
The half-grown chrysanthemums staring up like
   accusers,
Up through the streaked glass, flashing with sunlight,
A few white clouds all rushing eastward,
A line of elms plunging and tossing like horses,
And everyone, everyone pointing up and shouting!

Theodore Roethke

Daysies

Now have I thereto this condicioun
That, of alle the flowers in the mede,
Than love I most these flowres whyte and rede,
Swiche as men callen daysies in our toun.
To hem have I so greet affeccioun,
As I seyde erst, when comen is the May,
That in my bed ther daweth me no day
That I nam up, and walking in the mede
To seen these floures agein the sonne sprede,
Whan it up-riseth by the morwe shene,
The longe day, thus walking in the grene,
And whan the sonne ginneth for to weste,
Than closeth hit, and draweth hit to reste.

. . . lening on myn elbowe and my syde
The long day I shoop me for to abyde
Fir nothing elles, and I shal nat lye,
But for to loke upon the dayeseye,
That wel by reson men hit calle may
The 'dayeseye' or elles the 'ye of day,'
The emperice and flour of flours alle.
I pray to God that faire mot she falle,
And alle that Loven floures, for her sake!

Geoffrey Chaucer

The Lily

The modest Rose puts forth a thorn,
The humble Sheep a threatening horn;
While the Lily white shall in Love delight,
Nor a thorn, nor a threat, stain her beauty bright.

William Blake

The Dandelion's pallid tube
Astonishes the Grass,
And Winter instantly becomes
An infinite Alas –

The tube uplifts a signal Bud
And then a shouting Flower,–
The Proclamation of the Suns
That sepulture is o'er.

Emily Dickinson

Mist in the Meadows

The evening o'er the meadow seems to stoop
More distant lessens the diminished spire
Mist in the hollows reaks and curdles up
Like fallen clouds that spread – and things retire
Less seen and less – the shepherd passes near
And little distant most grotesquely shades
As walking without legs – lost to his knees
As through the rawky creeping smoke he wades
Now half way up the arches disappear
And small the bits of sky that glimmer through
Then trees loose all but tops – while fields remain
As wont – the indistinctness passes bye
The shepherd all his length is seen again
And further on the village meets the eye.

John Clare

The Fog

I saw the fog grow thick
    Which soon made blind my ken;
It made tall men of boys,
    And giants of tall men.

It clutched my throat, I coughed;
    Nothing was in my head
Except two heavy eyes
    Like balls of burning lead.

And when it grew so black
    That I could know no place,
I lost all judgement then
    Of distance and of space.

The street lamps, and the lights
    Upon the halted cars,
Could either be on earth
    Or be the heavenly stars.

A man passed by me close,
    I asked my way, he said,
'Come, follow me, my friend' –
    I followed where he led.

He walked the stones in front,
    'Trust me,' he said, 'and come':
I followed like a child –
    A blind man led me home.

W H Davies

The fog comes
on little cat feet.
It sits looking
over harbor and city
on silent haunches
and then moves on.

Carl Sandburg

November Night, Edinburgh

The night tinkles like ice in glasses.
Leaves are glued to the pavement with frost.
The brown air fumes at the shop windows,
Tries the doors, and sidles past.

I gulp down winter raw. The heady
Darkness swirls with tenements.
In a brown fuzz of cottonwool
Lamps fade up crags, die into pits.

Frost in my lungs is harsh as leaves
Scraped up on paths. I look up, there,
A high roof sails, at the mast-head
Fluttering a grey and ragged star.

The world's a bear shrugged in his den.
It's snug and close in the snoring night.
And outside like chrysanthemums
The fog unfolds its bitter scent.

Norman MacCaig

Friday Morning

It was on a Friday morning that they took me from the
  cell,
And I saw they had a carpenter to crucify as well:
You can blame it on to Pilate, you can blame it on the
  Jews,
You can blame it on the devil, but it's God I accuse.

'It's God they ought to crucify instead of you and me,'
I said it to the carpenter a-hanging on the tree.

You can blame it on to Adam, you can blame it on to
  Eve,
You can blame it on the apple, but that I can't believe;
It was God who made the devil and the woman and
  the man,
But there wouldn't be an apple if it wasn't in the plan.

Now Barabbas was a killer, and they let Barabbas go,
But you are being crucified for nothing here below,
And God is up in heaven, but he doesn't do a thing,
With a million angels watching, and they never move
  a wing.

'To hell with Jehovah!' to the carpenter I said,
'I wish that a carpenter had made the world instead.
  Good-bye and good luck to you, our ways they will
  divide,
Remember me in heaven, the man you hung beside.'

Sydney Carter

The Carol of the Poor Children

We are the poor children, come out to see the sights
On this day of all days, on this night of nights,
The stars in merry parties are dancing in the sky,
A fine star, a new star, is shining on high!

We are the poor children, our lips are frosty blue,
We cannot sing our carol as well as rich folk do,
Our bellies are so empty we have no singing voice,
But this night of all nights good children must rejoice.

We do rejoice, we do rejoice, as hard as we can try,
A fine star, a new star is shining in the sky!
And while we sing our carol, we think of the delight
The happy kings and shepherds make in Bethlehem
    tonight.

Are we naked, mother, and are we starving-poor –
Oh, see what gifts the kings have brought outside the
    stable door,
Are we cold, mother, the ass will give his hay
To make the manger warm and keep the cruel winds
    away.

We are the poor children, but not so poor who sing
Our carol with our voiceless hearts to greet the
    new-born king,
On this night of all nights, when in the frosty sky
A new star, a kind star is shining on high!

Richard Middleton

Epitaph in Lydford Churchyard

Here lies in a horizontal position the outside case of

GEORGE ROUTLEDGE, WATCHMAKER

Integrity was the mainspring and prudence
the regulator of all the actions of his life;
humane, generous and liberal,
His hand never stopped till he had relieved distress.

So nicely regulated were his movements that
he never went wrong, except when set going by
people who did not know his key.
Even then he was easily set right again.
He had the art of disposing his time so well,
till his hours glided away, his pulse
stopped beating.

He ran down November 14, 1801, aged 57,
In hopes of being taken in hand by his Maker,
Thoroughly cleaned, repaired, wound up, and set
going in the world to come, when time shall be no
more.

Song

When I am dead, my dearest,
  Sing no sad songs for me;
Plant thou no roses at my head,
  Nor shady cypress tree:
Be the green grass above me
  With showers and dewdrops wet;
And if thou wilt, remember,
  And if thou wilt, forget.

I shall not see the shadows,
  I shall not feel the rain;
I shall not hear the nightingale
  Sing on, as if in pain:
And dreaming through the twilight
  That doth not rise nor set,
Haply I may remember,
  And haply may forget.

Christina Rossetti

43

IN MEMORY OF

WILLIAM PICKERING,

who died Dec.ʳ 24. 1845
AGED 30 YEARS.

ALSO RICHARD EDGER

who died Dec.ʳ 24. 1845
AGED 24 YEARS.

THE SPIRITUAL RAILWAY

The Line to heaven by Christ was made
With heavenly truth the Rails are laid,
From Earth to Heaven the Line extends,
To Life Eternal where it ends.
Repentance is the Station then
Where Passengers are taken in
No Fee for them is there to pay
For Jesus is himself the way.
God's Word is the first Engineer
It points the way to Heaven so clear,
Through tunnels dark and dreary here
It does the way to Glory steer.
God's Love the Fire, his Truth the Steam,
Which drives the Engine and the Train,
All you who would to Glory ride,
Must come to Christ, in him abide
In First, and Second, and Third Class,
Repentance, Faith and Holiness,
You must the way to Glory gain
Or you with Christ will not remain.
Come then poor Sinners, now's the time
At any Station on the Line,
If you'll repent and turn from sin
The Train will stop and take you in.

Requiem

Under the wide and starry sky,
Dig the grave and let me lie.
Glad did I live and gladly die,
    And I laid me down with a will.

This be the verse you grave for me:
Here he lies where he longed to be;
Home is the sailor, home from sea,
    And the hunter home from the hill.

Robert Louis Stevenson

Here lies a poor woman who always was tired,
    She lived in a house where no help wasn't hired.
The last words she said were 'Dear friends, I am going,
    Where washing ain't wanted, nor mending, nor
    sewing.
There all things is done just exact to my wishes,
    For where folk don't eat there's no washing of
    dishes.
In Heaven loud anthems for ever are ringing,
    But having no voice, I'll keep clear of the singing.
Don't mourn for me now, don't mourn for me never;
    I'm going to do nothing for ever and ever.'

An Inscription by the Sea

(after the Greek of Glaucos)

No dust have I to cover me,
    My grave may no man show;
My tomb is this unending sea,
    And I lie far below.
My fate, O stranger, was to drown;
And where it was the ship went down
    Is what the sea-birds know.

The Express

After the first powerful plain manifesto
The black statement of pistons, without more fuss
But gliding like a queen, she leaves the station.
Without bowing and with restrained unconcern
She passes the houses which humbly crowd outside,
The gasworks, and at last the heavy page
Of death, printed by gravestones in the cemetery.
Beyond the town there lies the open country
Where, gathering speed, she acquires mystery,
The luminous self-possession of ships on ocean.
It is now she begins to sing – at first quite low
Then loud, and at last with a jazzy madness –
The song of her whistle screaming at curves,
Of deafening tunnels, brakes, innumerable bolts.
And always light, aerial, underneath,
Retreats the elate metre of her wheels.
Steaming through metal landscape on her lines,
She plunges new eras of white happiness,
Where speed throws up strange shapes, broad curves
And parallels clean like the steel of guns.
At last, further than Edinburgh or Rome,
Beyond the crest of the world, she reaches night
Where only a low streamline brightness
Of phosphorus on the tossing hills is white.
Ah, like a comet through flame she moves entranced
Wrapt in her music no bird song, no, nor bough
Breaking with honey buds, shall ever equal.

Stephen Spender

A Local Train of Thought

Alone, in silence, at a certain time of night,
Listening, and looking up from what I'm trying to
  write,
I hear a local train along the Valley. And 'There
Goes the one-fifty', think I to myself; aware
That somehow its habitual travelling comforts me,
Making my world seem safer, homelier, sure to be
The same to-morrow; and the same, one hopes, next
  year.
'There's peacetime in that train.' One hears it
  disappear
With needless warning whistle and rail-resounding
  wheels.
'That train's quite like an old familiar friend', one feels.

Siegfried Sassoon

Tremors

We took turns at laying
An ear on the rail –
So that we could tell
By the vibrations

When a train was coming.
Then we'd flatten ourselves
To the banks, scorched
Vetch and hedge-parsley,

While the iron flanks
Rushed past, sending sparks
Flying. It is more and more
A question of living

With an ear to the ground:
The tremors, when they come,
Are that much greater –
For ourselves, and others.

Nor is it any longer
A game, but a matter
Of survival: each explosion
Part of a procession

There can be no stopping.
Though the end is known,
There is nothing for it
But to keep listening . . .

Stewart Conn

49

Midnight on the Great Western

In the third-class seat sat the journeying boy,
   And the roof-lamp's oily flame
Played down on his listless form and face,
Bewrapt past knowing to what he was going,
   Or whence he came.

In the band of his hat the journeying boy
   Had a ticket stuck; and a string
Around his neck bore the key of his box,
That twinkled gleams of the lamp's sad beams
   Like a living thing.

What past can be yours, O journeying boy
   Towards a world unknown,
Who calmly, as if incurious quite
On all at stake, can undertake
   This plunge alone?

Knows your soul a sphere, O journeying boy
   Our rude realms far above,
Whence with spacious vision you mark and mete
This region of sin that you find you in
   But are not of?

Thomas Hardy

Corner Seat

Suspended in a moving night
The face in the reflected train
Looks at first sight as self-assured
As your own face. But look again.
Windows between you and the world
Keep out the cold, keep out the fright.
Then why does your reflection seem
So lonely in the moving night?

Louis MacNeice

To a Fat Lady Seen from the Train

O why do you walk through the fields in gloves,
    Missing so much and so much?
O fat white woman whom nobody loves,
Why do you walk through the fields in gloves,
When the grass is soft as the breast of doves
    And shivering-sweet to the touch?
O why do you walk through the fields in gloves,
    Missing so much and so much.

Frances Cornford

The Fear of Flowers

The nodding oxeye bends before the wind,
The woodbine quakes lest boys their flowers should
   find,
And prickly dogrose spite of its array
Can't dare the blossom-seeking hand away,
While thistles wear their heavy knobs of bloom
Proud as a warhorse wears its haughty plume,
And by the roadside danger's self defy;
On commons where pined sheep and oxen lie
In ruddy pomp and ever thronging mood
It stands and spreads like danger in a wood,
And in the village street where meanest weeds
Can't stand untouched to fill their husks with seeds,
The haughty thistle o'er all danger towers,
In every place the very wasp of flowers.

John Clare

Thistledown

Silver against blue sky
These ghosts of day float by,
Fitful, irregular,
Each one a silk-haired star,
Till from the wind's aid freed
They settle on their seed.

Not by the famished light
Of a moon-ridden night
But by clear sunny hours
Gaily these ghosts of flowers
Will rise and swirl and fall
Dance to their burial.

Andrew Young

Thistle

Thistle, blue bunch of daggers
rattling upon the wind,
saw-tooth that separates
the lips of grasses.

Your wound in childhood was
a savage shock of joy
that set the bees on fire
and the loud larks singing.

Your head enchanted then
smouldering among the flowers
filled the whole sky with smoke
and sparks of seed.

Now from your stabbing bloom's
nostalgic point of pain
ghosts of those summers rise
rustling across my eyes.

Seeding a magic thorn
to prick the memory,
to start in my icy flesh
fevers of long lost fields.

Laurie Lee

Thistles

Against the rubber tongues of cows and the hoeing
  hands of men
Thistles spike the summer air
Or crackle open under a blue-black pressure.

Every one a revengeful burst
Of resurrection, a grasped fistful
Of splintered weapons and Icelandic frost thrust up

From the underground stain of a decayed Viking.
They are like pale hair and the gutturals of dialects.
Every one manages a plume of blood.

Then they grow grey, like men.
Mown down, it is a feud. Their sons appear,
Stiff with weapons, fighting back over the same
  ground.

Ted Hughes

Thistles

Half grown before half seen,
like urchins in armour
double their size they stand
their ground boldly, their keen
swords out. But the farmer
ignores them. Not a hand

will he lift to cut them down:
they are not worth his switch
he says. Uncertain whom
they challenge, having grown
into their armour, each
breaks out a purple plume.

Under this image
of their warrior blood
they make a good death,
meeting the farmer's blade
squarely in their old age.
White then as winter breath

from every white head
a soul springs up. The wind
is charged with spirits: no –
not spirits of the dead
for these are living, will land
at our backs and go

to ground. Farmer and scythe
sing to each other. He
cannot see how roots writhe
underfoot, how the sons
of this fallen infantry
will separate our bones.

Jon Stallworthy

Think of this tower-block
as if it was a street standing up
and instead of toing and froing
in buses and cars
you up and down it
in a high speed lift.

There will be no pavement artists of course
because there aren't any pavements.
There isn't room for a market
but then there isn't room for cars.
No cars: no accidents
but don't lean
out of the windows
don't play in the lifts
or they won't work.
They don't work
and they won't work
if you play Split Kipper,
Fox and Chickens, Dittyback,
Keek-bogle, Jackerback,
Huckey-buck, Hotchie-pig,
Foggy-plonks, Ching Chang Cholly
or Bunky-Bean Bam-Bye.

Go down. The stairs are outside –
you can't miss them – try not to miss them, please.
No pets.
Think how unhappy they'd be
locked in a tower-block.
There will be
no buskers, no hawkers
no flowers, no chinwaggers
no sandwich boards,
no passers-by,
except for
low-flying aircraft
or high-flying sparrows.

Here is a note from Head Office:
you will love your neighbour
left right above below
so no music, creaky boots,
caterwauling somersaulting –
never never never jump up or down
or you may
never never never get down or up again.
No questions.
It's best to tip-toe,
creep, crawl, and whisper.
If there *are* any
problems phone me
and I'll be out.
Good day.

Michael Rosen

Number 14

That house you took me to
as a child, with its steps down
from the pavement into a doorway
that smelled of damp, along a passage
into a parlour with a black-leaded grate
and a brace of partridge in white
porcelain, that house
where you grew up under your father's belt –
I pass it every day, and up till now
I have watched the street it stood in
fall to the bulldozers, house by house
each day a bit more sky:
old man, the bulldozers have gone away
but your house is still there
its red front door still saying Number 14
its windows hooded with corrugated iron
jagged against the sky; its time come
and gone, waiting for one more stroke.

Keith Bosley

The Hammers

Noise of hammers once I heard,
Many hammers, busy hammers,
Beating, shaping, night and day,
Shaping, beating dust and clay
To a palace; saw it reared;
Saw the hammers laid away.

And I listened, and I heard
Hammers beating, night and day,
In the palace newly reared,
Beating it to dust and clay:
Other hammers, muffled hammers,
Silent hammers of decay.

Ralph Hodgson

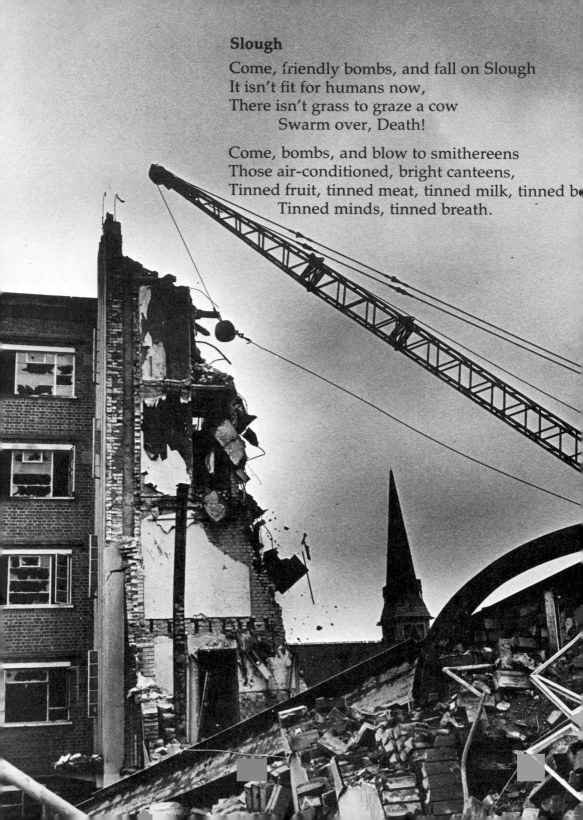

Slough

Come, friendly bombs, and fall on Slough
It isn't fit for humans now,
There isn't grass to graze a cow
  Swarm over, Death!

Come, bombs, and blow to smithereens
Those air-conditioned, bright canteens,
Tinned fruit, tinned meat, tinned milk, tinned be
  Tinned minds, tinned breath.

Mess up the mess they call a town –
A house for ninety-seven down
And once a week a half a crown
    For twenty years,

And get that man with double chin
Who'll always cheat and always win,
Who washes his repulsive skin
    In women's tears,

And smash his desk of polished oak
And smash his hands so used to stroke
And stop his boring dirty joke
    And make him yell.

But spare the bald young clerks who add
The profits of the stinking cad;
It's not their fault that they are mad,
    They've tasted Hell.

It's not their fault they do not know
The birdsong from the radio,
It's not their fault they often go
    To Maidenhead.

And talk of sports and makes of cars
In various bogus Tudor bars
And daren't look up and see the stars
    But belch instead.

In labour-saving homes, with care
Their wives frizz out peroxide hair
And dry it in synthetic air
    And paint their nails.

Come, friendly bombs, and fall on Slough
To get it ready for the plough.
The cabbages are coming now:
    The earth exhales.

John Betjeman

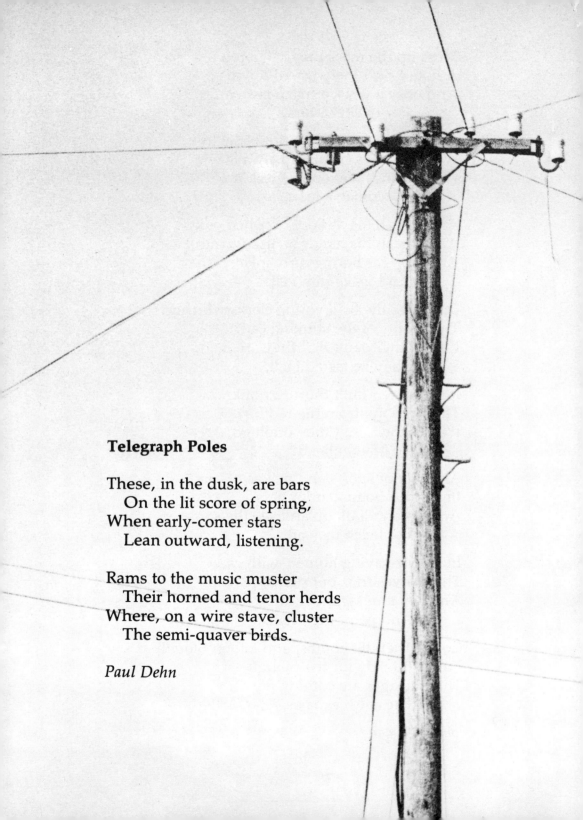

Telegraph Poles

These, in the dusk, are bars
   On the lit score of spring,
When early-comer stars
   Lean outward, listening.

Rams to the music muster
   Their horned and tenor herds
Where, on a wire stave, cluster
   The semi-quaver birds.

Paul Dehn

The Pylons

The secret of these hills was stone, and cottages
Of that stone made,
And crumbling roads
That turned on sudden hidden villages.

Now over these small hills they have built the concrete
That trails black wire:
Pylons, those pillars
Bare like nude, giant girls that have no secret.

The valley with its gilt and evening look
And the green chestnut
Of customary root,
Are mocked dry like the parched bed of a brook.

But far above and far as sight endures
Like whips of anger
With lightning's danger
There runs the quick perspective of the future.

This dwarfs our emerald country by its trek
So tall with prophecy:
Dreaming of cities
Where often clouds shall lean their swan-white neck.

Stephen Spender

Once at Piertarvit

Once at Piertarvit,
one day in April,
the edge of spring,
with the air a-ripple,
a sea like knitting,
as Avril and Ann
and Ian and I
walked in the wind
along the headland,
Ian threw an apple
high over Piertarvit.

Not a great throw,
you would say, if you saw it,
but good for Ian.
His body tautened,
his arm let go
like a flesh-and-bone bow,
and the hard brown apple
left over from autumn
flew up and up,
crossing our gaze
from the cliff at Piertarvit.

Then, all at once, horror
glanced off our eyes,
Ann's, mine, Avril's.
As the apple curved
in the stippled sky,
at the top of its arc,
it suddenly struck
the shape of a bird –
a gull that had glided
down from nowhere
above Piertarvit.

We imagined the thud
and the thin ribs breaking,
blood, and the bird
hurtling downward.
No such thing.
The broad wings wavered
a moment only,
then air sustained them.
The gull glided on
while the apple fell
in the sea at Piertarvit.

Nobody laughed.
Nobody whistled.
In that one moment,
our world had faltered.
The four of us stood
stock-still with horror,
till, breaking the spell,
Ian walked away
with a whirl in his head.
The whole sky curdled
over Piertarvit.

I followed slowly,
with Ann and Avril
trailing behind.
We had lost our lightness.
Even today,
old as we are,
we would find it hard
to say, without wonder,
'Ian hit a bird
with an apple, in April,
once at Piertarvit.'

Alastair Reid

69

Song

I had a dove and the sweet dove died;
And I have thought it died of grieving:
O, what could it grieve for? Its feet were tied,
With a silken thread of my own hand's weaving;
Sweet little red feet! why should you die –
Why should you leave me, sweet bird! why?
You lived alone in the forest-tree,
Why, pretty thing! would you not live with me?
I kissed you oft and gave you white peas;
Why not live sweetly, as in the green trees?

John Keats

Numbers

A thousand and fifty-one waves
Two hundred and thirty-one seagulls
A cliff of four hundred feet
Three miles of ploughed fields
One house
Four windows look on the waves
Four windows look on the ploughed fields
One skylight looks on the sky
In that skylight's sky is one seagull.

Stevie Smith

The Dog Lovers

So they bought you
And kept you in a
Very good home
Central heating
TV
A deep freeze
A *very* good home –
No one to take you
For that lovely long run –
But otherwise
'A *very* good home'.
They fed you Pal and Chum
But not that lovely long run,
Until, mad with energy and boredom
You escaped – and ran and ran and ran
Under a car.
Today they will cry for you –
Tomorrow they will buy another dog.

Spike Milligan

My Mother saw a Dancing Bear

My mother saw a dancing bear
By the schoolyard, a day in June.
The keeper stood with chain and bar
And whistle pipe, and played a tune.

And bruin lifted up its head
And lifted up its dusty feet,
And all the children laughed to see
It caper in the summer heat.

They watched as for the Queen it died.
They watched it march. They watched it halt.
They heard the keeper as he cried,
'Now, roly-poly!' 'Somersault!'

And then, my mother said, there came
The keeper with a begging-cup,
The bear with burning coat of fur,
Shaming the laughter to a stop.

They paid a penny for the dance,
But what they saw was not the show;
Only, in bruin's aching eyes,
Far-distant forests, and the snow.

Charles Causley

Song of the Battery Hen

We can't grumble about accommodation:
we have a new concrete floor that's
always dry, four walls that are
painted white, and a sheet-iron roof
the rain drums on. A fan blows warm air
beneath our feet to disperse the smell
of chicken-shit and, on dull days,
fluorescent lighting sees us.

You can tell me: if you come by
the North door, I am in the twelfth pen
on the left-hand side of the third row
from the floor; and in that pen
I am usually the middle one of three.
But, even without directions, you'd
discover me. I have the same orange-
red comb, yellow beak and auburn
feathers, but as the door opens and you
hear above the electric fan a kind of
one-word wail, I am the one
who sounds loudest in my head.

Listen. Outside this house there's an
orchard with small moss-green apple
trees; beyond that, two fields of
cabbages; then, on the far side of
the road, a broiler house. Listen:
one cockerel grows out of there, as
tall and proud as the first hour of sun.
Sometimes I stop calling with the others
to listen, and wonder if he hears me.

The next time you come here, look for me.
Notice the way I sound inside my head.
God made us all quite differently,
and blessed us with this expensive home.

Edwin Brock

One summer evening (led by her) I found
A little boat tied to a willow tree
Within a rocky cave, its usual home.
Straight I unloosed her chain, and stepping in
Pushed from the shore. It was an act of stealth
And troubled pleasure, nor without the voice
Of mountain-echoes did my boat move on;
Leaving behind her still, on either side,

Small circles glittering idly in the moon,
Until they melted all into one track
Of sparkling light. But now, like one who rows,
Proud of his skill, to reach a chosen point
With an unswerving line, I fixed my view
Upon the summit of a craggy ridge,
The horizon's utmost boundary; far above
Was nothing but the stars and the grey sky.
She was an elfin pinnace; lustily
I dipped my oars into the silent lake,
And, as I rose upon the stroke, my boat
Went heaving through the water like a swan;
When, from behind that craggy steep till then
The horizon's bound, a huge peak, black and huge,
As if with voluntary power instinct
Upreared its head. I struck and struck again,
And growing still in stature the grim shape
Towered up between me and the stars, and still,
For so it seemed, with purpose of its own
And measured motion like a living thing,
Strode after me. With trembling oars I turned,
And through the silent water stole my way
Back to the covert of the willow tree;
There in her mooring-place I left my bark, –
And through the meadows homeward went, in grave
And serious mood; but after I had seen
That spectacle, for many days, my brain
Worked with a dim and undetermined sense
Of unknown modes of being; o'er my thoughts
There hung a darkness, call it solitude
Or blank desertion. No familiar shapes
Remained, no pleasant images of trees,
Of sea or sky, no colours of green fields;
But huge and mighty forms, that do not live
Like living men, moved slowly through the mind
By day, and were a trouble to my dreams.

William Wordsworth from *The Prelude*

Stanzas

When a man hath no freedom to fight for at home,
  Let him combat for that of his neighbours;
Let him think of the glories of Greece and of Rome
  And get knocked on the head for his labours.

To do good to mankind is the chivalrous plan,
  And is always as nobly requited;
Then battle for freedom wherever you can,
  And, if not shot or hanged, you'll get knighted.

Lord Byron

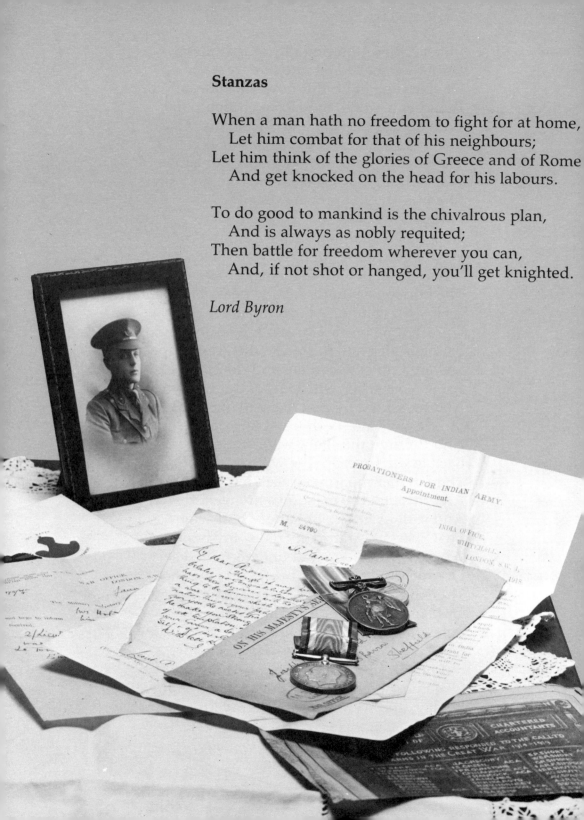

Harp Song of the Dane Women

What is a woman that you forsake her,
And the hearth-fire and the home-acre,
To go with the old grey Widow-maker?

She has no house to lay a guest in –
But one chill bed for all to rest in,
That the pale suns and the stray bergs nest in:

She has no strong white arms to fold you,
But the ten-times-fingering weed to hold you –
Out on the rocks where the tide has rolled you.

Yet, when the signs of summer thicken,
And the ice breaks, and the birch-buds quicken,
Yearly you turn from our side, and sicken –

Sicken again for the shouts and the slaughters.
You steal away to the lapping waters,
And look at your ship in her winter-quarters.

You forget our mirth, and talk at the tables,
The kine in the shed and the horse in the stables –
To pitch her sides and go over her cables.

Then you drive out where the storm-clouds swallow,
And the sound of your oar-blades, falling hollow,
Is all we have left through the months to follow.

Ah, what is Woman that you forsake her,
And the hearth-fire and the home-acre,
To go with the old grey Widow-maker?

Rudyard Kipling

Abbey Tomb

I told them not to ring the bells
The night the Vikings came
Out of the sea and passed us by
The fog was thick as cream
And in the abbey we stood still
As if our breath might blare
Or pulses rattle if we once
Stopped staring at the door.

Through the walls and through the fog
We heard them passing by.
The deafer monks thanked God too soon
And later only I
Could catch the sound of prowling men
Still present in the hills
So everybody else agreed
To ring the abbey bells.

And even while the final clang
Still snored upon the air,
And while the ringers joked their way
Down round the spiral stair,
Before the spit of fervent prayer
Had dried into the stone
The raiders came back through the fog
And killed us one by one.

Father Abbot at the altar
Lay back with his knees
Doubled under him, caught napping
In the act of praise.
Brother John lay unresponsive
In the warming room.
The spiders came out for the heat
And then the rats for him.

Under the level of the sheep
Who graze here all the time
We lie now, under tourists' feet
Who in good weather come.
I told them not to ring the bells
But centuries of rain
And blustering have made their tombs
Look just as right as mine.

Patricia Beer

The War Song of Dinas Vawr

The mountain sheep are sweeter,
But the valley sheep are fatter;
We therefore deemed it meeter
To carry off the latter.
We made an expedition;
We met a host, and quelled it;
We forced a strong position,
And killed the men who held it.

On Dyfed's richest valley,
Where herds of kine were brousing,
We made a mighty sally,
To furnish our carousing.
Fierce warriors rushed to meet us;
We met them, and o'erthrew them:
They struggled hard to beat us;
But we conquered them, and slew them.

As we drove our prize at leisure,
The king marched forth to catch us:
His rage surpassed all measure,
But his people could not match us.
He fled to his hall-pillars;
And, ere our force we led off,
Some sacked his house and cellars,
While others cut his head off.

We there, in strife bewildering,
Spilt blood enough to swim in:
We orphaned many children,
And widowed many women.
The eagles and the ravens
We glutted with our foemen;
The heroes and the cravens,
The spearmen and the bowmen.

We brought away from battle,
And much their land bemoaned them,
Two thousand head of cattle,
And the head of him who owned them:
Ednyfed, king of Dyfed,
His head was borne before us;
His wine and beasts supplied our feasts,
And his overthrow, our chorus.

Thomas Love Peacock

On the Late Massacre in Piedmont

Avenge, O Lord, thy slaughtered saints, whose bones
  Lie scattered on the Alpine mountains cold,
  Even them who kept thy truth so pure of old
  When all our fathers worshipped stocks and stones,
Forget not; in thy book record their groans
  Who were thy sheep, and in their ancient fold
  Slain by the bloody Piedmontese that rolled
  Mother with infant down the rocks. Their moans
The vales redoubled to the hills, and they
  To heaven. Their martyred blood and ashes sow
  O'er all the Italian fields, where still doth sway
The triple tyrant, that from these may grow
  A hundredfold, who, having learnt thy way,
  Early may fly the Babylonian woe.

John Milton

On the Massacre of Glencoe

'O tell me, Harper, wherefore flow
Thy wayward notes of wail and woe,
Far down the desert of Glencoe,
 Where none may list their melody?
Say, harp'st thou to the mists that fly,
Or to the dun-deer glancing by,
Or to the eagle, that from high
 Screams chorus to thy minstrelsy?' –

'No, not to these, for they have rest, –
The mist-wreath has the mountain-crest,
The stag his lair, the erne her nest,
 Abode of lone security.
But those for whom I pour the lay,
Not wild-wood deep, nor mountain gray,
Not this deep dell, that shrouds from day,
 Could screen from treach'rous cruelty.

'Their flag was furl'd, and mute their drum,
The very household dogs were dumb,
Unwont to bay at guests that come
 In guise of hospitality.
His blithest notes the piper plied,
Her gayest snood the maiden tied,
The dame her distaff flung aside,
 To tend her kindly housewifery.

'The hand that mingled in the meal,
At midnight drew the felon steel,
And gave the host's kind breast to feel
 Meed for his hospitality!
The friendly hearth which warm'd that hand,
At midnight arm'd it with the brand,
That bade destruction's flames expand
 Their red and fearful blazonry.

'Then woman's shriek was heard in vain,
Nor infancy's unpitied plain,
More than the warrior's groan, could gain
   Respite from ruthless butchery!
The winter wind that whistled shrill,
The snows that night that cloked the hill,
Though wild and pitiless, had still
   Far more than Southern clemency.

'Long have my harp's best notes been gone.
Few are its strings, and faint their tone,
They can but sound in desert lone
   Their gray-hair'd master's misery.
Were each gray hair a minstrel string,
Each chord should imprecations fling,
Till startled Scotland loud should ring,
   'Revenge for blood and treachery!''

Sir Walter Scott

Oh stay at home, my lad, and plough
   The land and not the sea,
And leave the soldiers at their drill,
And all about the idle hill
   Shepherd your sheep with me.

Oh stay with company and mirth
   And daylight and the air;
Too full already is the grave
Of fellows that were good and brave
   And died because they were.

A E Housman

Icarus Allsorts

*'A meteorite is reported to have landed
in New England. No damage is said . . .'*

A littlebit of heaven fell
From out the sky one day
It landed in the ocean
Not so very far away
The General at the radar screen
Rubbed his hands with glee
And grinning pressed the button
That started World War Three.

From every corner of the earth
Bombs began to fly
There were even missile jams
No traffic lights in the sky
In the time it takes to blow your nose
The people fell, the mushrooms rose

'House!' cried the fatlady
As the bingohall moved to various parts
of the town

'Raus!' cried the German butcher
as his shop came tumbling down

Philip was in the countinghouse
Counting out his money
The Queen was in the parlour
Eating bread and honey
When through the window
Flew a bomb
And made them go all funny
(By the way if you're wondering
What happened to the maid
Well in this particular raid

She lost more than her nose
In fact she came to a close
Or so the story goes.)

In the time it takes to draw a breath
Or eat a toadstool, instant death.

The rich
Huddled outside the doors of their fallout shelters
Like drunken carolsingers

The poor
Clutching shattered televisions
And last week's editions of T.V. Times
(but the very last)

Civil defence volunteers
With their tin hats in one hand
And their heads in the other

CND supporters
Their ban the bomb mojos beginning to rust
Have scrawled 'I told you so' in the dust.

A littlebit of heaven fell
From out the sky one day
It landed in Vermont
North-Eastern U.S.A.
The general at the radar screen
He should have got the sack
But that wouldn't bring
Three thousand million, seven hundred, and
  sixty-eight people back,
Would it?

Roger McGough

Meeting at Night

The grey sea and the long black land;
And the yellow half-moon large and low;
And the startled little waves that leap
In fiery ringlets from their sleep,
As I gain the cove with pushing prow,
And quench its speed i' the slushy sand.

Then a mile of warm sea-scented beach;
Three fields to cross till a farm appears;
A tap at the pane, the quick sharp scratch
And blue spurt of a lighted match,
And a voice less loud, through its joys and fears,
Than the two hearts beating each to each!

Robert Browning

My mistress' eyes are nothing like the sun;
Coral is far more red than her lips' red:
If snow be white, why then her breasts are dun;
If hairs be wires, black wires grow on her head.
I have seen roses damask'd, red and white,
But no such roses see I in her cheeks;
And in some perfumes is there more delight
Than in the breath that from my mistress reeks.
I love to hear her speak, yet well I know
That music hath a far more pleasing sound:
I grant I never saw a goddess go, –
My mistress, when she walks, treads on the ground:
And yet, by heaven, I think my love as rare
As any she belied with false compare.

William Shakespeare

The Prince of Love

How sweet I roamed from field to field,
    And tasted all the summer's pride,
'Till I the prince of love beheld,
    Who in the sunny beams did glide!

He showed me lilies for my hair,
    And blushing roses for my brow;
He led me through his gardens fair,
    Where all his golden pleasures grow.

With sweet May dews my wings were wet,
    And Phoebus fired my vocal rage;
He caught me in his silken net,
    And shut me in his golden cage.

He loves to sit and hear me sing,
    Then, laughing, sports and plays with me;
Then stretches out my golden wing,
    And mocks my loss of liberty.

William Blake

A Dream

Once in a dream (for once I dreamed of you)
    We stood together in an open field;
    Above our heads two swift-winged pigeons
    wheeled,
Sporting at ease and courting full in view.
When loftier still a broadening darkness flew,
    Down-swooping, and a ravenous hawk revealed;
    Too weak to fight, too fond to fly, they yield;
So farewell life and love and pleasures new.
Then as their plumes fell fluttering to the ground,
    Their snow-white plumage flecked with crimson
    drops,
      I wept, and thought I turned towards you to
    weep:
    But you were gone; while rustling hedgerow tops
Bent in a wind which bore to me a sound
    Of far-off piteous bleat of lambs and sheep.

Christina Rossetti

A Red, Red Rose

My love is like a red, red rose
   That's newly sprung in June:
My love is like the melody
   That's sweetly played in tune.

As fair art thou, my bonnie lass,
   So deep in love am I:
And I will love thee still, my dear,
   Till a' the seas gang dry.

Till a' the seas gang dry, my dear,
   And the rocks melt wi' the sun:
And I will love thee still, my dear,
   While the sands o' life shall run.

And fare thee weel, my only love,
   And fare thee weel a while!
And I will come again, my love,
   Thou' it were ten thousand mile.

Robert Burns

91

First Love

I ne'er was struck before that hour
  With love so sudden and so sweet,
Her face it bloomed like a sweet flower
  And stole my heart away complete.
My face turned pale as deadly pale,
  My legs refused to walk away,
And when she looked, what could I ail?
  My life and all seemed turned to clay.

And then my blood rushed to my face
  And took my eyesight quite away,
The trees and bushes round the place
  Seemed midnight at noonday.
I could not see a single thing,
  Words from my eyes did start –
They spoke as chords do from the string,
  And blood burnt round my heart.

Are flowers the winter's choice?
  Is love's bed always snow?
She seemed to hear my silent voice,
  Not love's appeals to know.
I never saw so sweet a face
  As that I stood before.
My heart has left its dwelling-place
  And can return no more.

John Clare

Lines

The cold earth slept below,
  Above the cold sky shone;
And all around, with a chilling sound,
  From caves of ice and fields of snow,
  The breath of night like death did flow
    Beneath the sinking moon.

The wintry hedge was black,
  The green grass was not seen.
The birds did rest on the bare thorn's breast,
  Whose roots, beside the pathway track,
  Had bound their folds o'er many a crack,
    Which the frost had made between.

Thine eyes glowed in the glare
  Of the moon's dying light;
As a fenfire's beam on a sluggish stream
  Gleams dimly, so the moon shone there,
  And it yellowed the strings of thy raven hair,
    That shook in the wind of night.

The moon made thy lips pale, beloved –
  The wind made thy bosom chill –
The night did shed on thy dear head
  Its frozen dew, and thou didst lie
  Where the bitter breath of the naked sky
    Might visit thee at will.

Percy Bysshe Shelley

The Passionate Shepherd to his Love

Come live with me, and be my love,
And we will all the pleasures prove
That hills and valleys, dales and fields,
And all the craggy mountains yield.

There we will sit upon the rocks,
Seeing the shepherds feed their flocks
By shallow rivers, to whose falls
Melodious birds sing madrigals.

And I will make thee beds of roses
With a thousand fragrant posies,
A cap of flowers and a kirtle
Embroider'd all with leaves of myrtle.

A gown made of the finest wool
Which from our pretty lambs we pull,
Fair lined slippers for the cold,
With buckles of the purest gold;

A belt of straw and ivy buds,
With coral clasps and amber studs,
And if these pleasures may thee move,
Come live with me, and be my love.

The shepherd swains shall dance and sing
For thy delight each May-morning:
If these delights thy mind may move,
Then live with me, and be my love.

Christopher Marlowe

Come Live with Me

He. Come live with me and we'll be drovers;
When stars are lambing in the rivers,
By couples we will count the sheep
Yet kiss before we go to sleep.

All summer down the Lachlan-side
We'll sing like Clancy as we ride
Till hawks hang charmed above the plain
And shearing-time comes in again.

For love of you I'll ring the shed,
Then we'll have breakfast served in bed
By slattern maids in cotton caps,
And go to work at noon perhaps.

She. And in a basket I will keep
The skirtings of the finest sheep
For spinning tights for ballet-girls
With combs and cutters in their curls;

And they will dance at each smoke-o
For your delight upon the toe
And bring you beer and violets
In garlands for your gallon hats.

With mistletoe I'll crown my hair
And sing most sweetly to the air,
'Since Time's a shearer, where's the sin
In kissing in the super-bin?'

David Campbell

95

To His Coy Mistress

Had we but world enough, and time,
This coyness, Lady, were no crime.
We would sit down and think which way
To walk and pass our long love's day.
Thou by the Indian Ganges' side
Shouldst rubies find: I by the tide
Of Humber would complain. I would
Love you ten years before the Flood,
And you should, if you please, refuse
Till the conversion of the Jews.
My vegetable love should grow
Vaster than empires, and more slow;
An hundred years should go to praise
Thine eyes and on thy forehead gaze;
Two hundred to adore each breast;
But thirty thousand to the rest;
An age at least to every part,
And the last age should show your heart;
For, Lady, you deserve this state,
Nor would I love at lower rate.
   But at my back I always hear
Time's wingèd chariot hurrying near;
And yonder all before us lie
Deserts of vast eternity.
Thy beauty shall no more be found,
Nor, in thy marble vault, shall sound
My echoing song: then worms shall try
That long preserved virginity,
And your quaint honour turn to dust,
And into ashes all my lust:
The grave's a fine and private place,
But none, I think, do there embrace.

Now therefore, while the youthful hue
Sits on thy skin like morning dew,
And while thy willing soul transpires
At every pore with instant fires,
Now let us sport us while we may,
And now, like amorous birds of prey,
Rather at once our time devour
Than languish in his slow-chapt power.
Let us roll all our strength and all
Our sweetness up into one ball,
And tear our pleasures with rough strife
Thorough the iron gates of life:
Thus, though we cannot make our sun
Stand still, yet we will make him run.

Andrew Marvell

Evans

Evans? Yes, many a time
I came down his bare flight
Of stairs into the gaunt kitchen
With its wood fire, where crickets sang
Accompaniment to the black kettle's
Whine, and so into the cold
Dark to smother in the thick tide
Of night that drifted about the walls
Of his stark farm on the hill ridge.

It was not the dark filling my eyes
And mouth appalled me; not even the drip
Of rain like blood from the one tree
Weather-tortured. It was the dark
Silting the veins of that sick man
I left stranded upon the vast
And lonely shore of his bleak bed.

R S Thomas

Plastic Woman

What are you saying
Supermarket shopping lady
In the scarlet telephone box?
Lady with a shopping bag
Full of labelled pollution with secret codes
What are you saying?
Is this your dream booth?
Are you telling some plastic operator
You are Princess Grace
And can he put you through
to Buckingham Palace?
Two decimal pence
Is very little to pay for a dream in Catford.
If only the label on the door didn't say
'Out of Order'.
Shouldn't it be on you?

Spike Milligan

Upstream

I often go back
to my little song,
and hum it patiently
at my fishing-hole on the ice.
Again and again,
I hum that simple little song.
I, who all too soon
get weary when I fish,
watchfully angling,
trying to tempt
the blue-black salmon with their glossy scales,
who swim,
    upstream.

Blowingly cold, my vigil on the ice.
I soon give up
When I get home with insufficient catch
I say it was the fish that failed,
    upstream.

Yet it's wonderful to roam
the snow-soft river-ice,
as long as I support myself,
    upstream.

But now my life has slid
far from the height of the mountain-tops,
deep into the valley of old age,
    upstream.

If I hunt on land,
or try to fish,
it isn't long
before I'm sinking to my knees,
stricken with weariness,
    upstream.

I'll never feel
the surge of strength I used to get,
when I hunt inland
for my hut and those I feed,
    upstream.

I'm just a worn-out hunter now,
who'll never breathe
the great winds of the hunting-grounds again.

Yet my body's still alive
and my stomach still craves
feasts of meat.

My manhood is reduced:
an unblest fisherman,
who makes his hole
in sea or river ice,
where no trout bite,
    upstream.

Yet life is full
of interest and excitement!
I only . . .
I only have my song,
though it too glides away from me,
    upstream.

For I'm just an ordinary hunter
who never inherited singing
from the bird-song of the sky.

Ikinilik

The Astigmatic

At seven the sun that lit my world blew out
Leaving me only mist. Through which I probed
My way to school, guessed wildly at the sums
Whose marks on the board I couldn't even see.

They wanted to send me away to a special school.
I refused, and coped as best I could with half
The light lost in the mist, screwing my tears
Into my work, my gritted teeth, my writing –

Which crawled along and writhed. Think thoughts at
  will,
None of it comes across. Even now friends ask
'How do you read that scrawl?' The fact is, I don't;
Nobody could. I guess. But how would you

Like my world where parallels actually join,
Perspectives vary at sight? Once in a pub
I walked towards a sign marked gents over
A grating and crashed through the floor –

Well, it looked all right to me. Those steep stairs
People told me of later flattened to lines
In my half-world. The rest imagination
Supplied: when you've half a line you extend it.

The lenses drag their framework down my nose.
I still can't look strangers in the face,
Wilting behind a wall of glass at them.
It makes me look shifty at interviews.

I wake up with a headache, chew all day
Aspirins, go to bed dispirited,
Still with a dull pain somewhere in my skull,
And sleep. Then, in my dreams, the sun comes out.

Philip Hobsbaum

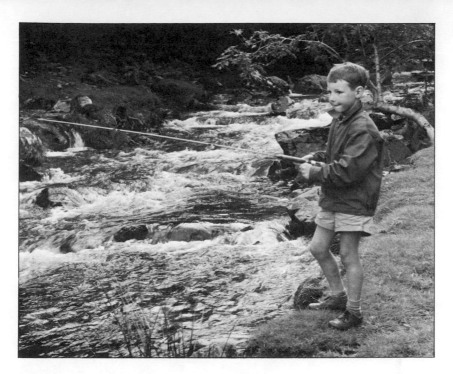

Who?

Who is that child I see wandering, wandering
Down by the side of the quivering stream?
Why does he seem not to hear, though I call to him?
Where does he come from, and what is his name?

Why do I see him at sunrise and sunset
Taking, in old-fashioned clothes, the same track?
Why, when he walks, does he cast not a shadow
Though the sun rises and falls at his back?

Why does the dust lie so thick on the hedgerow
By the great field where a horse pulls the plough?
Why do I see only meadows, where houses
Stand in a line by the riverside now?

Why does he move like a wraith by the water,
Soft as the thistledown on the breeze blown?
When I draw near him so that I may hear him,
Why does he say that his name is my own?

Charles Causley

Schoolmistress (Miss Humm)

Straight-backed as a Windsor chair
She stood on the top playground step
And surveyed her Saturnalian kingdom.
At 8.45 precisely, she stiffened
(If that were possible), produced a key
– A large, cold dungeon-key –
Placed it below her lip, and blew.
No summons from Heaven itself
(It was a church school) was more imperious!
No angel trumpet or Mosean thunder-clap
Calling the Israelites to doom or repentance
Met swifter obedience. No Gorgon
Suspended life with such efficiency.
In the middle of a shout, a scream,
We halted. Our faces froze.
No longer George or Tom or Mary,
But forty reproductions of a single child,
Chilled to conformity. We gathered
Like captive troops and, climbing steps,
Received the inspection of her cool eyes,
Willing them away from unwashed necks
Or black-ringed fingernails,
But knowing our very thoughts were visible
If she chose to see. Nothing escaped her.
She was (as I said, a church school)
God, St Michael, the Recording Angel
And, in our guiltier moments, Lucifer –
A Lucifer in long tweed skirts
And a blouse severely fastened at the neck
By a round cameo that was no ornament
But the outward sign of inward authority.
Even the Rector, when he stepped inside
And the brown walls rumbled to his voice,
Dwindled to a curate . . .
It would have astonished us to learn, I think,
That she ate supper, went to bed,
And even, perhaps, on occasions, slept.

Clive Sansom

An Elementary School Class Room in a Slum

Far far from gusty waves, these children's faces.
Like rootless weeds the torn hair round their paleness.
The tall girl with her weighed-down head. The paper-
Seeming boy with rat's eyes. The stunted unlucky heir
Of twisted bones, reciting a father's gnarled disease,
His lesson from his desk. At back of the dim class,
One unnoted, sweet and young: His eyes live in a
    dream
Of squirrels' game, in tree room, other than this.

On sour cream walls, donations. Shakespeare's head
Cloudless at dawn, civilized dome riding all cities.
Belled, flowery, Tyrolese valley. Open-handed map
Awarding the world its world. And yet, for these
Children, these windows, not this world, are world,
Where all their future's painted with a fog,
A narrow street sealed in with a lead sky,
Far far from rivers, capes, and stars of words.

Surely Shakespeare is wicked, the map a bad example
With ships and sun and love tempting them to steal –
For lives that slyly turn in their cramped holes
From fog to endless night? On their slag heap, these
    children
Wear skins peeped through by bones and spectacles of
    steel
With mended glass, like bottle bits on stones.
All of their time and space are foggy slum
So blot their maps with slums as big as doom.

Unless, governor, teacher, inspector, visitor,
This map becomes their window and these windows
That open on their lives like crouching tombs
Break, O break open, till they break the town
And show the children to the fields and all their world
Azure on their sands, to let their tongues
Run naked into books, the white and green leaves
   open
The history theirs whose language is the sun.

Stephen Spender

You'd better believe him

A fable

Discovered an old rocking-horse in Woolworth's,
He tried to feed it but without much luck
So he stroked it, had a long conversation about
The trees it came from, the attics it had visited.
Tried to take it out then
But the store detective he
Called the store manager who
Called the police who in court next morning said
'He acted strangely when arrested,
 His statement read simply "I believe in
   rocking-horses".
 We have reason to believe him mad.'
'Quite so,' said the prosecution,
'Bring in the rocking-horse as evidence.'
'I'm afraid it's escaped sir,' said the store manager,
'Left a hoof-print as evidence
 On the skull of the store detective.'
'Quite so,' said the prosecution, fearful
 of the neighing
 Out in the corridor.

Brian Patten

Good Taste

Travelling, a man met a tiger, so . . .
He ran. The tiger ran after him
Thinking: How fast I run . . . But

The road thought: How long I am . . . Then
They came to a cliff, yes, the man
Grabbed at an ash root and swung down

Over its edge. Above his knuckles, the tiger.
At the foot of the cliff, its mate. Two mice,
One black, one white, began to gnaw the root.

And by the traveller's head grew one
Juicy strawberry, so . . . hugging the root
The man reached out and plucked the fruit.

How sweet it tasted!

Christopher Logue

There is no Frigate like a Book
To take us Lands away
Nor any Coursers like a Page
Of prancing Poetry –
This Traverse may the poorest take
Without oppress of Toll –
How frugal is the Chariot
That bears the Human soul.

Emily Dickinson

A Brown Paper Carrierbag

IN THE TIME . . .

   a spider's web woven across
the plateglass window shivers snaps
and sends a shimmering haze of lethal stars
across the crowded restaurant

IN THE TIME IT TAKES . . .

   jigsaw pieces of shrapnel
glide gently towards children
tucking in   to the warm flesh
a terrible hunger sated

IN THE TIME IT TAKES TO PUT DOWN . . .

   on the pavement
people come apart   slowly
at first
only the dead not screaming

IN THE TIME IT TAKES TO PUT DOWN
A BROWN PAPER CARRIERBAG.

Roger McGough

New Members Welcome

Pull the blinds
   on your emotions
Switch off your face.
Put your love into neutral
This way to the human race.

Spike Milligan

The Qualification

wurk aw yir life
nuthnty show
pit oanthi nyuze
same awl drivl

yoonyin bashn
wurkir bashn
lord this
sir soan soa thaht

shood hearma boay
sayzwi need gunz
an armd revalooshn
nuthn else wurks

awright fur him thoa
uppit thi yooni
tok aw yi like therr
thats whit its fur

Tom Leonard

The Future

The young boy stood looking up the road
to the future. In the distance both sides
appeared to converge together. 'That
is due to perspective, when you reach
there the road is as wide as it is here',
said an old wise man. The young
boy set off on the road, but,
as he went on, both sides of the
road converged until he could
go no further. He returned to ask
the old man what to do, but
the old man was dead.

Spike Milligan

The Hangman at Home

What does the hangman think about
When he goes home at night from work?
When he sits down with his wife and
Children for a cup of coffee and a
Plate of ham and eggs, do they ask
Him if it was a good day's work
And everything went well or do they
Stay off some topics and talk about
The weather, baseball, politics
And the comic strips in the papers
And the movies? Do they look at his
Hands when he reaches for the coffee
Or the ham and eggs? If the little
Ones say, Daddy, play horse, here's
A rope – does he answer like a joke:
I seen enough rope for today?
Or does his face light up like a
Bonfire of joy and does he say:
It's a good and dandy world we live
In. And if a white face moon looks
In through a window where a baby girl
Sleeps and the moon-gleams mix with
Baby ears and baby hair – the hangman –
How does he act then? It must be easy
For him. Anything is easy for a hangman,
I guess.

Carl Sandburg

On moonlit heath and lonesome bank
   The sheep beside me graze;
And yon the gallows used to clank
   Fast by the four cross ways.

A careless shepherd once would keep
   The flocks by moonlight there,
And high amongst the glimmering sheep
   The dead man stood on air.

They hang us now in Shrewsbury jail:
   The whistles blow forlorn,
And trains all night groan on the rail
   To men that die at morn.

There sleeps in Shrewsbury jail to-night.
   Or wakes, as may betide,
A better lad, if things went right,
   Than most that sleep outside.

And naked to the hangman's noose
   The morning clocks will ring
A neck God made for other use
   Than strangling in a string.

And sharp the link of life will snap,
   And dead on air will stand
Heels that held up as straight a chap
   As treads upon the land.

So here I'll watch the night and wait
   To see the morning shine,
When he will hear the stroke of eight
   And not the stroke of nine;

And wish my friend as sound a sleep
   As lads I did not know,
That shepherded the moonlit sheep
   A hundred years ago.

A E Housman

Rizpah

Wailing, wailing, wailing, the wind over land and
    sea –
And Willy's voice in the wind, 'O mother, come
    out to me.'
Why should he call me to-night, when he knows
    that I cannot go?
For the downs are as bright as day, and the full
    moon stares at the snow.

We should be seen, my dear; they would spy us
    out of the town.
The loud black nights for us, and the storm
    rushing over the down,
When I cannot see my own hand, but am led by
    the creak of the chain,
And grovel and grope for my son till I find myself
    drenched with the rain.

Anything fallen again? nay – what was there left
    to fall?
I have taken them home, I have number'd the
    bones, I have hidden them all.
What am I saying? and what are *you*? do you
    come as a spy?
Falls? what falls? who knows? As the tree falls so
    must it lie.

Who let her in? how long has she been? you –
    what have you heard?
Why did you sit so quiet? you never have spoken
    a word.
O – to pray with me – yes – a lady – none of their
    spies –
But the night has crept into my heart, and begun
    to darken my eyes.

Ah – you, that have lived so soft, what should *you*
   know of the night,
The blast and the burning shame and the bitter
   frost and the fright?
I have done it, while you were asleep – you were
   only made for the day.
I have gather'd my baby together – and now you
   may go your way.

Nay – for it's kind of you, Madam, to sit by an old
   dying wife.
But say nothing hard of my boy, I have only an
   hour of life.
I kiss'd my boy in the prison, before he went out
   to die.
'They dared me to do it,' he said, and he never
   has told me a lie.
I whipt him for robbing an orchard once when he
   was but a child –
'The farmer dared me to do it,' he said; he was
   always so wild –
And idle – and he couldn't be idle – my Willy – he
   never could rest.
The King should have made him a soldier, he
   would have been one of his best.

But he lived with a lot of wild mates, and they
   never would let him be good;
They swore that he dare not rob the mail, and he
   swore that he would;
And he took no life; but he took one purse, and
   when all was done
He flung it among his fellows – I'll none of it, said
   my son.

I came into court to the Judge and the lawyers. I
   told them my tale,

God's own truth – but they kill'd him, they kill'd
  him for robbing the mail.
They hang'd him in chains for a show – we had
  always borne a good name –
To be hang'd for a thief – and then put away –
  isn't that enough shame?
Dust to dust – low down – let us hide! but they
  set him so high
That all the ships of the world could stare at him,
  passing by.
God 'ill pardon the hell-black raven and horrible
  fowls of the air,
But not the black heart of the lawyer who kill'd
  him and hang'd him there.

And the jailer forced me away. I had bid him my
  last goodbye;
They had fasten'd the door of his cell. 'O mother!'
  I heard him cry.
I couldn't get back tho' I tried, he had something
  further to say,
And now I never shall know it. The jailer forced
  me away.

Then since I couldn't but hear that cry of my boy
  that was dead,
They seized me and shut me up: they fasten'd me
  down on my bed.
'Mother, O mother!' – he call'd in the dark to me
  year after year –
They beat me for that, they beat me – you know
  that I couldn't but hear;
And then at the last they found I had grown so
  stupid and still
They let me abroad again – but the creatures had
  worked their will.

Flesh of my flesh was gone, but bone of my bone
  was left –

I stole them all from the lawyers – and you, will
    you call it a theft? –
My baby, the bones that had suck'd me, the
    bones that had laughed and had cried –
Theirs? O no! they are mine – not theirs – they
    had moved in my side.

Do you think I was scared by the bones? I kiss'd
    em, I buried 'em all –
I can't dig deep, I am old – in the night by the
    churchyard wall.
My Willy 'ill rise up whole when the trumpet of
    judgment 'ill sound,
But I charge you never to say that I laid him in
    holy ground.

And if *he* be lost – but to save *my* soul, that is all
    your desire:
Do you think that I care for *my* soul if my boy be
    gone to the fire?
I have been with God in the dark – go, go, you
    may leave me alone –
You never have borne a child – you are just as
    hard as a stone.

Madam, I beg your pardon! I think that you mean
    to be kind,
But I cannot hear what you say for my Willy's
    voice in the wind –
The snow and the sky so bright – he used but to
    call in the dark,
And he calls to me now from the church and not
    from the gibbet – for hark!
Nay – you can hear it yourself – it is coming –
    shaking the walls –
Willy – the moon's in a cloud – Goodnight. I am
    going. He calls.

Alfred, Lord Tennyson

Haunted

Evening was in the wood, louring with storm.
A time of drought had sucked the weedy pool
And baked the channels; birds had done with song.
Thirst was a dream of fountains in the moon,
Or willow-music blown across the water
Leisurely sliding on by weir and mill.

Uneasy was the man who wandered, brooding,
His face a little whiter than the dusk.
A drone of sultry wings flicker'd in his head.
The end of sunset burning thro' the boughs
Died in a smear of red; exhausted hours
Cumber'd, and ugly sorrows hemmed him in.

He thought: 'Somewhere there's thunder,' as he
      strove
To shake off dread; he dared not look behind him,
But stood, the sweat of horror on his face.

He blunder'd down a path, trampling on thistles,
In sudden race to leave the ghostly trees.
And: 'Soon I'll be in open fields,' he thought,
And half remembered starlight on the meadows,
Scent of mown grass and voices of tired men,
Fading along the field-paths; home and sleep
And cool-swept upland spaces, whispering leaves,
And far off the long churring night-jar's note.
But something in the wood, trying to daunt him,
Led him confused in circles through the thicket.
He was forgetting his old wretched folly,
And freedom was his need; his throat was choking.
Barbed brambles gripped and clawed him round his
      legs,
And he floundered over snags and hidden stumps.
Mumbling: 'I will get out! I must get out!'
Butting and thrusting up the baffling gloom,
Pausing to listen in a space 'twixt thorns,
He peers around with peering, frantic eyes.

An evil creature in the twilight looping,
Flapped blindly in his face. Beating it off,
He screeched in terror, and straightway something
      clambered
Heavily from an oak, and dropped, bent double,
To shamble at him zigzag, squat and bestial.

Headlong he charges down the wood, and falls
With roaring brain – agony – the snap't spark –
And blots of green and purple in his eyes.
Then the slow fingers groping on his neck,
And at his heart the strangling clasp of death.

Siegfried Sassoon

Now the hungry lion roars,
    And the wolf behowls the moon;
Whilst the heavy ploughman snores,
    All with weary task fordone,
Now the wasted brands do glow,
    Whilst the screech-owl, screeching loud,
Puts the wretch that lies in woe
    In remembrance of a shroud.
Now it is the time of night
    That the graves, all gaping wide,
Every one lets forth his sprite,
    In the church-way paths to glide:
And we fairies, that do run
    By the triple Hecate's team,
From the presence of the sun,
    Following darkness like a dream,
Now are frolic; not a mouse
Shall disturb this hallow'd house;
I am sent with broom before,
To sweep the dust behind the door.

William Shakespeare

The Witches' Charm

The owl is abroad, the bat, and the toad,
    And so is the cat-a-mountain;
The ant and the mole sit both in a hole,
    And frog peeps out o'the fountain;
The dogs they do bay, and the timbrels play,
    The spindle is now a-turning;
The moon it is red, and the stars are fled,
    But all the sky is a-burning:
The ditch is made, and our nails the spade,
With pictures full, of wax and of wool;
Their livers I stick with needles quick:
There lacks but the blood to make up the flood.

Ben Jonson

Pegasus

From the blood of Medusa
Pegasus sprang.
His hoof of heaven
Like melody rang.
His whinny was sweeter
Than Orpheus' lyre,
The wing on his shoulder
Was brighter than fire.

His tail was a fountain,
His nostrils were caves,
His mane and his forelock
Were musical waves,
He neighed like a trumpet,
He cooed like a dove,
He was stronger than terror
And swifter than love.

He could not be captured,
He could not be bought,
His rhythm was running,
His standing was thought.
With one eye on sorrow
And one eye on mirth
He galloped in heaven
And gambolled on earth.

And only the poet
With wings to his brain
Can mount him and ride him
Without any rein,
The stallion of heaven
The steed of the skies,
The horse of the singer
Who sings as he flies.

Eleanor Farjeon

The Man in the Bowler Hat

I am the unnoticed, the unnoticeable man:
The man who sat on your right in the morning train:
The man you looked through like a windowpane:
The man who was the colour of the carriage, the colour
   of the mounting
Morning pipe smoke.

I am the man too busy with living to live,
Too hurried and worried to see and smell and touch:
The man who is patient too long and obeys too much
And wishes too softly and seldom.

I am the man they call the nation's backbone,
Who am boneless – playable catgut, pliable clay:
The Man they label Little lest one day
I dare to grow.

I am the rails on which the moment passes,
The megaphone for many words and voices:
I am graph, diagram,
Composite face.

I am the led, the easily-fed,
The tool, the not-quite fool,
The would-be-safe-and-sound,
The uncomplaining bound,
The dust fine-ground,
Stone-for-a-statue waveworn pebble-round.

A S J Tessimond

Simplify me when I'm Dead

Remember me when I am dead
and simplify me when I'm dead.

As the processes of earth
strip off the colour and the skin:
take the brown hair and blue eye

and leave me simpler than at birth,
when hairless I came howling in
as the moon entered the cold sky.

Of my skeleton perhaps,
so stripped, a learned man will say
'He was of such a type and intelligence,' no more.

Thus when in a year collapse
particular memories, you may
deduce, from the long pain I bore

the opinions I held, who was my foe
and what I left, even my appearance
but incidents will be no guide.

Time's wrong-way telescope will show
a minute man ten years hence
and by distance simplified.

Through that lens see if I seem
substance or nothing: of the world
deserving mention or charitable oblivion,

not by momentary spleen
or love into decision hurled,
leisurely arrive at an opinion.

Remember me when I am dead
and simplify me when I'm dead.

Keith Douglas

Acknowledgements

The editors and publisher acknowledge permission to use the following copyright poems:

Patricia Beer: 'Abbey Tomb' from *Just Like The Resurrection* (Macmillan). Reprinted by permission of the author. **John Betjeman:** 'Slough' from *Collected Poems*. Reprinted by permission of John Murray (Publishers) Ltd. **Keith Bosley:** 'Number 14' (copyright © 1979 Keith Bosley) from *Young British Poets* (Chatto). Reprinted by permission of the author. **Edwin Brock:** 'Song of the Battery Hen' from *Song of the Battery Hen* (Secker & Warburg). Reprinted by permission of David Higham Associates Ltd. **David Campbell:** 'Come Live With Me and We'll be Drovers' from *Selected Poems*. Reprinted by permission of the author's literary estate and Angus & Robertson (UK) Ltd. **Sydney Carter:** 'Friday Morning' from *Greenprint for Song*. Reprinted by permission of Stainer & Bell Ltd. **Charles Causley:** 'My Mother Saw a Dancing Bear' from *Collected Poems* and 'Who' from *Figgie Hobbin* (both Macmillan). Reprinted by permission of David Higham Associates Ltd. **Stewart Conn:** 'Tremors' from *Ear To The Ground*. Reprinted by permission of Hutchinson Publ. Group Ltd. **Frances Cornford:** 'To a Fat Lady Seen from the Train' from *Collected Poems* (Barrie & Jenkins). Reprinted by permission of Hutchinson Publ. Group Ltd. **W. H. Davies:** 'The Fog' from *The Complete Poems of W. H. Davies*. Reprinted by permission of the Executors of the W. H. Davies Estate and Jonathan Cape Ltd. **Paul Dehn:** 'Telegraph Poles' from *The Fern on The Rock* (copyright © Dehn Enterprises Ltd., 1965, 1976). Reprinted by permission of Hamish Hamilton, London. **Keith Douglas:** 'Simplify Me When I'm Dead' from *The Complete Poems of Keith Douglas* (edited by Desmond Graham 1978). Reprinted by permission of Oxford University Press. **Eleanor Farjeon:** 'Pegasus' from *Collected Poems* Michael Joseph Ltd). Reprinted by permission of David Higham Associates Ltd. **Philip Hobsbaum:** 'The Astigmatic' from *In Retreat* (Macmillan). Reprinted by permission of the author. **Ralph Hodgson:** 'The Hammers' from *Collected Poems*. Reprinted by permission of Mrs. Hodgson and Macmillan, London and Basingstoke. **A. E. Housman:** 'Oh, stay at home . . .' and 'On moonlit heath . . .' (Poems XXXVIII and IX) from *Collected Poems* (Cape). Reprinted by permission of The Society of Authors as the literary representatives of the Estate of A. E. Housman. **Ted Hughes:** 'Thistles' from *Wodwo*. Reprinted by permission of Faber & Faber Ltd. **Ikinilik:** 'Upstream' from *Eskimo Poems From Canada and Greenland* (translated by Tom Lowenstein). Reprinted by permission of Allison & Busby Ltd. **T. H. Jones:** 'Advice to a Knight' from *The Colour of Cockcrowing*. Reprinted by permission of Granada Publishing Ltd. **Laurie Lee:** 'Thistle' from *The Bloom of Candles* (Hogarth Press). Reprinted by permission of the author. **Tom Leonard:** 'The Qualification' from *Bunnit Husslin* (Third Eye Centre, Glasgow). Reprinted by permission of the author. **C. Logue:** 'Good Taste' from *Songs* (Hutchinson). Reprinted by permission of Hope Leresche & Sayle. **Norman MacCaig:** 'Fetching Cows' from *Measures*. Reprinted by permission of Chatto & Windus Ltd. 'November Night, Edinburgh' from *The Sinai Sort*. Reprinted by permission of The Hogarth Press Ltd. **Roger McGough:** 'Icarus Allsorts' (copyright © 1967 by Roger McGough) from *Penguin Modern Poets 10*, and 'A Brown Paper Bag' (copyright © 1976 by Roger McGough) from *In The Classroom* (Cape). Both reprinted by permission of Hope Leresche and Sayle. **Spike Milligan:** 'The Dog Lovers', 'Plastic Woman', 'New Members Welcome' and 'The Future', all from *Small Dreams of a Scorpion*. Reprinted by permission of Michael Joseph Ltd. **Harold Monro:** 'Milk for the cat' from *Collected Poems*. Reprinted by permission of Gerald Duckworth & Co. Ltd. **Edwin Morgan:** 'Glasgow October 1972' from *A Sense of Belonging* (Blackie). Reprinted by permission of the author. **Brian Patten:** 'You'd better believe him' from *Notes to the Hurrying Man*. Reprinted by permission of George Allen & Unwin Ltd. **Alistair Reid:** 'Once at Piertarvit' from *Oddments, Inklings, Omens, Moments* (Little, Brown & Co.). Reprinted by permission of Laurence Pollinger Ltd. **Edwin Arlington Robinson:** 'An Inscription by the Sea' ('Variations of Greek Themes', XI), from *Collected Poems* (copyright 1915 by Edwin Arlington Robinson, renewed 1943 by Ruth Nivison). Reprinted by permission of Macmillan Publishing Co., Inc. **Theodore Roethke:** 'Child on top of a greenhouse' from *The Collected Poems of Theodore Roethke*. Reprinted by permission of Faber & Faber Ltd. **Michael Rosen:** 'Think of this tower block', 'I Went to the Doctor' and 'Here is the News' all from *Wouldn't You Like to Know*. 'Saturdays I put my boots on' from *Mind Your Own Business*. All reprinted by permission of André Deutsch Ltd. **Carl Sandburg:** 'Fog' from *Chicago Poems* (copyright 1916 by Holt, Rinehart and Winston, Inc.; copyright 1944 by Carl Sandburg). 'The Hangman at Home' from *Smoke and Steel* (copyright by permission of Harcourt Brace Jovanovich, Inc. **Clive Sansom:** 'Schoolmistress (Miss Humm)' from *Dorset Village* (Methuen). Reprinted by permission of David Higham Associates Ltd. **Siegfried Sassoon:** 'A Local Train of Thought' and 'Haunted' from *Collected Poems* (Faber). Both reprinted by permission of George T. Sassoon. **Stevie Smith:** 'The Forlorn Sea', 'The Galloping Cat' and 'Numbers' all from *The Collected Poems of Stevie Smith* (Allen Lane). Reprinted by permission of James MacGibbon as executor. **Stephen Spender:** 'The Express', 'The Pylons' and 'An Elementary School Classroom in a Slum', all from *Collected Poems*. Reprinted by permission of Faber & Faber Ltd. **Jon Stallworthy:** 'Thistles' from *Root and Branch*. Reprinted by permission of Chatto & Windus Ltd. **A. S. J. Tessimond:** 'The Man in the Bowler Hat' from *Not Love Perhaps* (Autolyous Press). Reprinted by permission of Hubert Nicolson as literary executor to ASJ Tessimond. **R. S. Thomas:** 'Evans' from *Selected Poems 1946–1968*. Reprinted by permission of Granada Publishing Ltd. **Andrew Young:** 'Thistledown' from *Complete Poems* (edited by Leonard Clark). Reprinted by permission of Martin Secker & Warburg Ltd.